COLOR MY OWN
DRAGON STORY

AN IMMERSIVE, CUSTOMIZABLE COLORING BOOK FOR KIDS
(THAT RHYMES!)

BRIAN C HAILES

GW00857920

For information about permission to reproduce selections from this book, please write Permissions, Epic Edge Publishing, 1934 Fielding Hill Ln, Draper, UT 84020.

www.epicedgepublishing.com

Library of Congress Cataloging-in-Publication Data
Color My Own Dragon Story: An Immersive, Customizable Coloring Book for Kids (That Rhymes!)
Written by Brian C Hailes

p. cm.

Summary: Venture into a world of fantasy, adventure, danger and excitement as you color your way through medieval lands full of dragons and other ancient monsters! Fly back in time to a place of knights, maidens, goblins and unicorns, but be wary and vigilant, for you never know what might be lurking around the high castle walls. Sharpen your coloring skills. Increase your knowledge of mythical beasts and the names of some of your favorite fantastic creatures. And customize the tale with your very own name and other characteristics to become the hero of your own rhyming dragon story! Bedtime will never be the same.

A fun, interactive coloring quest that will whisk you away into a time of heroes and the most formidable monsters imaginable! Grab your crayons, markers or pencils, and steady your sword and shield, little warriors. It's time to discover the real monsters that live beyond our imaginations. (Intended for kids ages 6-12 . . . or all kids at heart)

1. Childrens—Fiction. 2. Childrens—Dragons & Mythical Creatures
3. Childrens—Coloring Books
II. Hailes, Brian C., ill. III. Title.

Paperback ISBN-13: 978-1-951374-25-9
Hardback ISBN-13: 978-1-951374-26-6

Printed in the USA
Designed by Epic Edge Publishing

10 9 8 7 6 5 4 3 2 1

Whether or not dragons exist is not the right question,
but whether or not a dragon exists inside you.

— *B.C. Hailes*

COLOR MY OWN
DRAGON STORY

AN IMMERSIVE, CUSTOMIZABLE COLORING BOOK FOR KIDS
(THAT RHYMES!)

STARRING: _____

(your name)

I was lucky to be born

A magnificent Dragon,

In a place called _____ ,
(your favorite place)

Inside of a wagon.

The wagon belonged to a

Knight of the realm;

A kind man named _____ ,
(your guardian's name)

Who was as true as an Elm.

European Dragon

Krak's Dragon

He didn't hunt Dragons,

Or slay them, like some;

Or hate them, or fear them,

Or treat them like scum.

He revered them for all

Their diversity, power;

Their wisdom, their _____ ,
(fire, breath or teeth)

And their might to devour.

He had found my small egg
On the side of a road.
With no sign of my parents,
Nor nearby Dragon abode.

I hatched in his _____ ,
(arms, hands or lap)
Helpless, weak and alone.
So he made me a nest,
And he carried me home.

From whelp into fledgling,
I've since sought to find
More Dragons like me,
And my parents in kind.

Western Dragon Whelps

Sensing my need to

Return to the wild,

The knight set me loose

With a nod and warm smile.

Allowed to take to wing,

I pressed hard to fly high,

Searching for my _____ ,
(brothers, sisters or family)

I soared through the sky.

European Dragon

I have found many friends

In my ongoing travels,

But none quite like me . . .

And my patience unravels.

Some Dragons are friendly,

Or harmless or helpful;

And some can be _____ ,
(goofy, screwy or kooky)

Or downright forgetful.

Oriental Dragon

Some Dragons intimidate,

And can seem rather scary,

With teeth, claws and horns

Causing most to be wary.

Their sinuous bodies

That twist, curl or crawl

Their way into _____

(stories, myths or legends)

Are intriguing to all.

Lung Dragon

Greater Drake

Fat Dragon

Hydra

From some, I've found it best

To keep a good, healthy distance,

Like the Hydra with its several heads,

Flames and deathly resistance.

For unonwary _____
(wanderers, travelers, or warriors)

That encounter this beast,

I'm afraid they're quite likely

To become its next feast.

I do not mean to frighten,

Indeed, many Dragons are nice.

They're useful and loyal,

Full of wisdom and advice.

Though most are reclusive

And hole up in their caves,

Once you get to know them,

Their _____ comes in waves.
(zeal, zest or zing)

Dragonnet

American Dragon

I met huge Western Dragons
With wings and four legs,
And great, mighty Wyverns
With _____ horned heads.
(spiky, spiny or thorny)

Elder Dragon

Fire-Drake

I waved to a Cockatrice,

Knucker and Wyrm,

And flew over _____ ,
(Fire-Drakes or Ice-Drakes)

As their _____ made me squirm.
(heat or cold)

Amphiptere

I saw Quetzalcoatl,

A _____ Amphiptere
(feathered, spiked or scaly)

Oriental and African

Drakes far and near.

Knucker

Long Dragon

Fire Dragon

I even ran into a

Proud Northern Griffin

Whose eagle-like gaze

And sharp beak made me stiffen.

Some serpentine Dragons

Slither by just like snakes;

And some live in _____ ,
(deserts, forests or oceans)

In swamps or great lakes.

Griffin

Bull Dragon

Great Horned Dragon

My _____ has/have taught me:
(journey, quest or travels)

No matter the place,

We Dragons are a respectable,

Diversified race.

My family is scattered

All over the Earth;

And we all share a kinship

Spanning well beyond birth.

We are creatures unique;

By wing, tooth or claw,

Let the world stand agape,

And behold us in awe!

My name is _____ ,
(your name)

And I am a Dragon.

THE END

OTHER "COLOR MY OWN" TITLES NOW AVAILABLE!

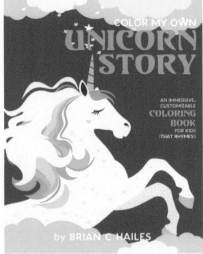

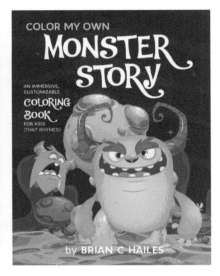

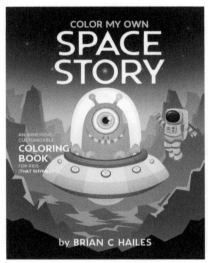

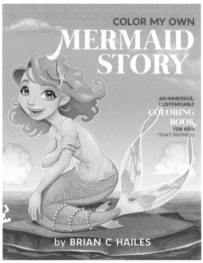

ABOUT THE AUTHOR

BRIAN C HAILES, creator of Draw It With Me (www.drawitwithme.com), is also the award-winning writer/ illustrator of over forty-five (and counting) novels, children's picture books, comics and graphic novels, including Blink: An Illustrated Spy Thriller Novel, Devil's Triangle, Dragon's Gait, Skeleton Play, Don't Go Near the Crocodile Ponds, If I Were a Spaceman, Here, There Be Monsters, Heroic, Passion & Spirit, Continuum (Arcana Studios), as well as McKenna, McKenna, Ready to Fly, and Grace & Sylvie: A Recipe for Family (American Girl), among others. In addition to his publishing credits, Hailes has also illustrated an extensive collection of fantasy, science fiction, and children's book covers as well as interior magazine illustrations. Hailes has received numerous awards for his works from across the country, including Winner of the L. Ron Hubbard Illustrators of the Future contest out of Hollywood. His artwork has also been featured in the 2017-2020 editions of Infected By Art.

Hailes studied illustration and graphic design at Utah State University where he received his Bachelor of Fine Arts degree, as well as the Academy of Art University in San Francisco.

He currently lives in Salt Lake City with his wife and four boys, where he continues to write, paint and draw regularly. More of his work can be seen at HailesArt.com

Other Titles Available from
Epic Edge Publishing

Illustrated Novels	Graphic Novels / Comics	Childrens Picture Books	Anthologies	Non-Fiction

Blink: An Illustrated Spy Thriller Novel
by Brian C Hailes

Avila
(Available 2021!)
by Robert J Defendi
& Brian C Hailes

Devil's Triangle: The Complete Graphic Novel
by Brian C Hailes
& Blake Casselman

Dragon's Gait
by Brian C Hailes

KamiKazi
by John English
& Brian C Hailes

If I Were a Spaceman: A Rhyming Adventure Through the Cosmos
by Brian C Hailes
& Tithi Luadthong

Here, There Be Monsters
by Brian C Hailes
& Tithi Luadthong

Don't Go Near the Crocodile Ponds
by Brian C Hailes

Skeleton Play
by Brian C Hailes

Can We Be Friends?
by Edie New
& Cindy Hailes

Cresting the Sun: A Sci-fi / Fantasy Anthology Featuring 12 Award-Winning Short Stories
by Brian C Hailes,
Rick Bennett
& Nicholas Adams

Heroic: Tales of the Extraordinary
by Blake Casselman,
David Farland,
Michael Stackpole
& more

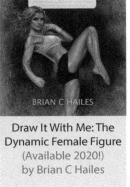

Draw It With Me: The Dynamic Female Figure
(Available 2020!)
by Brian C Hailes

DIWM 2020 Annual 1
(Available 2020!)
by Brian C Hailes,
Heather Edwards
& more

Passion & Spirit: The Dance Quote Book
by Brian C Hailes

Lightning Source UK Ltd.
Milton Keynes UK
UKHW051111140920
369869UK00004B/62